GARFIELD

SITTING PRETTY

JIM DAVIS

RAVETTE BOOKS

First published by Ravette Books Limited 1992

Printed and bound for
Ravette Books Limited
3 Glenside Estate, Star Road, Partridge Green,
Horsham, West Sussex RH13 8RA
An Egmont Company
by Proost International Bookproduction, Belgium

ISBN: 1 85304 400 8

A fridge too far

DINNERTIME!

HUNGRY, GARFIELD?

IS ODIE STUPID?

GREAT! LET'S GO TO THE REFRIGERATOR AND FIND SOMETHING TO EAT

© 1988 United Feature Syndicate, Inc.

COME ON, ODIE

DON'T DO IT, JON!

JIM DAVIS 10-30

I'D BETTER GO TO THE RESCUE

CLEAN OUT THE REFRIGERATOR, JON!

SLAM!

Roll on old age! Nobody expects you to take any exercise!

Currant affairs

GARFIELD, I'VE ALWAYS WONDERED, WHAT DO YOU DO WITH ALL THE RAISINS YOU PICK OFF YOUR COOKIES?

THAT'S NONE OF YOUR BUSINESS

OH WELL, I GUESS I'LL GO CLEAN OUT THE COAT CLOSET TODAY

I WOULDN'T DO THAT IF I WERE YOU

© 1988 United Feature Syndicate, Inc.

YAAAAHHH!!!

VERY FUNNY, GARFIELD

JIM DAVIS

JUST LOOK AT THE MESS YOU'VE MADE!

11-6

NOW I'LL HAVE TO GET A BROOM OUT OF THE BROOM CLOSET TO CLEAN THIS UP

I WOULDN'T DO THAT IF I WERE YOU

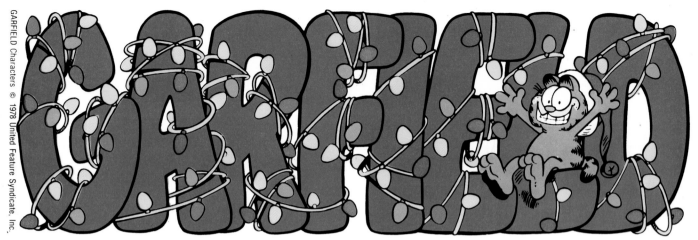

GARFIELD! WAIT!

MOST KINDS OF SPIDERS ARE COMPLETELY HARMLESS

JON,... YOU'RE RIGHT

ESPECIALLY THE DEAD KINDS!

JIM DAVIS 11-10

GARFIELD, I DON'T FEEL LIKE SCRATCHING YOUR BELLY

I HAVE BETTER THINGS TO DO

JIM DAVIS 11-11

LIKE MENDING YOUR SHREDDED SHIRT?

JIM DAVIS 11-12

BOMP!

I LOVE VOLLEYDOG

Every second counts

SOME PETS ARE WELL BEHAVED, AND THEN THERE ARE MY PETS. I CAN'T LEAVE THEM ALONE FOR A SECOND. WATCH THIS

SO LONG, BOYS! I'LL ONLY BE GONE FOR A SECOND!

JIM DAVIS 11-13

ONE

I REST MY CASE

AND HERE'S A PHOTO OF YOU WITH THE PIGS ON MY FOLK'S FARM LAST SUMMER

YOU'RE THE ONE WITH THE STRIPES

IT'S GIVING ME A HEADACHE

BOY, THIS EXERCISING IS TOUGH

TRY LOOSENING YOUR SWEAT-BAND

I CAN'T BELIEVE JUDY ASKED US TO LEAVE HER PARTY

BY THE WAY, WHAT WERE YOU DOING IN THE SALAD BOWL?

BOBBING FOR CROUTONS

BOY WAS SHE MAD

YOU'D THINK SHE'D NEVER HAD HAIR ON HER TOMATO WEDGES BEFORE

Drenched to the bone

Just practicing my tune. It's called, 'Wasn't me — honest!'

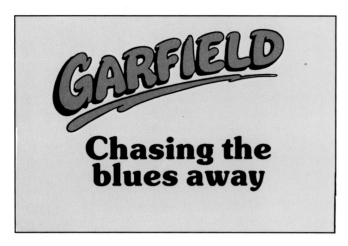

Cupboard love

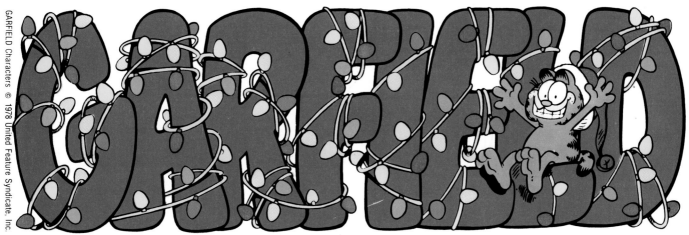

Food for thought

SMACK SLURP MUNCH

HEY, ODIE, DO YOU KNOW WHAT THEY PUT IN DOG FOOD?

DOG FOOD HAS LIZARDS AND YAK LIPS AND GUM THAT'S ALREADY BEEN CHEWED AND ALUMINUM SIDING...

AND SOME STUFF YOU WOULDN'T EVEN WANT TO KNOW ABOUT

GARFIELD! WE'RE OUT OF CAT FOOD. YOU'LL HAVE TO EAT DOG FOOD TODAY

OKAY

URP

WHAT'S WITH ODIE?

MUST HAVE BEEN SOMETHING HE ATE

Let's face it!

OH, VERY WELL, GARFIELD. YOU MAY HAVE MY STEAK

I KNOW. I'M A SUCKER FOR THE LOVING ADORATION OF A PET

JIM DAVIS   1-22

Kick-start

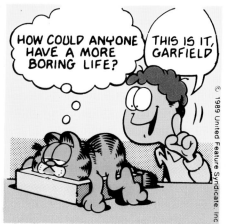

Thread alert

KNIT
KNIT
KNIT
KNIT
KNIT
KNIT
KNIT

HELLO, GARFIELD

CRASH!

PERHAPS MY LITTLE RUSE DIDN'T WORK

JIM DAVIS 2-5

RR
COMIC
ALBUMS

OTHER TITLES AVAILABLE IN THIS SERIES

GARFIELD

No. 2 Words Of Wisdom

HAGAR

No. 1 The Hero

LUCKY LUKE

No. 1 The Dalton Brothers
        Memory Game

MARMADUKE

No. 1 Canine Capers

PINK PANTHER

No. 1 Through The Hoop

SNOOPY

No. 1 Swings Into Action

THUNDERBIRDS

No. 1 To The Rescue
No. 2 In Space

TOM & JERRY

No. 1 Copy Cat
No. 2 Sweet Temptation

£3.99 each

Additional titles will be added to this series, for a complete list please contact
Ravette Books.

All these books are available at your local bookshop or newsagent, or can be ordered
direct from the publisher. Just tick the titles you require and fill in the form below. Prices
and availability subject to change without notice.

Ravette Books Limited, 3 Glenside Estate, Star Road, Partridge Green, Horsham,
West Sussex RH13 8RA

Please send a cheque or postal order and allow the following for postage and packing.
UK – 50p for one book and 35p for each additional book ordered.

Name ....

Address ....

          ....